Mother and Daughter Journal

Pass Back and Forth

How to use this Journal

This mom and daughter Journal is aimed at knowing each other in the best possible manner. There are no rules as to fill the questions asked. You are free to right in your own words for a keepsake.

This is a pass back and forth kind of journal consisting of prompts on each page to answer. Have fun knowing each other. Use this as a keepsake to have a look at this in future years.

THIS JOURNAL

belongs to

_____

&

_____

Start Date:

__/ __/ ____

Our Little Story Together!

Dear Mom

Things you love about me?

·Dear Daughter·

Things you love about me?

Dear Mom

The first thing you say to me in the morning is

·Dear Daughter·

The first thing you say to me in the morning is

Dear Mom

What are your goals for this year?

·Dear Daughter·

What are your goals for this year?

Dear Mom

What are the things you are grateful for?

·Dear Daughter·

What are the things you are grateful for?

Dear Mom

Your favourite thing to do all day?

_____

_____

_____

_____

_____

_____

_____

~· Dear Daughter ·~

Your favourite thing to do all day?

Dear Mom

What's your favourite quote?

·Dear Daughter·

What's your favourite quote?

Dear Mom

What makes you feel better about yourself?

·Dear Daughter·

What makes you feel better about yourself?

Dear Mom

What's your favourite memory with me?

·Dear Daughter·

What's your favourite memory with me?

Dear Mom

Describe your dream vacation..

·Dear Daughter·

Describe your dream vacation..

Dear Mom

If you could be invisible for one day what would you do?

·Dear Daughter·

If you could be invisible for one day what would you do?

Dear Mom

What is your favourite word? Why?

·Dear Daughter·

What is your favourite word? Why?

Dear Mom

What is the funniest joke you know?

∼ ·Dear Daughter· ∼

What is the funniest joke you know?

Dear Mom

Who is the coolest person you've ever met?

~·Dear Daughter·~

Who is the coolest person you've ever met?

Dear Mom

When do you feel the bravest?

·Dear Daughter·

When do you feel the bravest?

Dear Mom

What are you most scared of?

·Dear Daughter·

What are you most scared of?

Dear Mom

What is your favourite season? What do you love about it?

~. Dear Daughter .~

What is your favourite season? What do you love about it?

Dear Mom

What is your favourite kind of food?

Dear Daughter

What is your favourite kind of food?

Dear Mom

What kind of things make you feel cared for?

·Dear Daughter·

What kind of things make you feel cared for?

Dear Mom

What would you like to talk about?

·Dear Daughter·

What would you like to talk about?

Dear Mom

What makes you laugh?

Dear Daughter

What makes you laugh?

Dear Mom

What are the things that make you angry?

·Dear Daughter·

What are the things that make you angry?

Dear Mom

What is your biggest regret?

·Dear Daughter·

What is your biggest regret?

Dear Mom

What are you proud of?

~·Dear Daughter·~

What are you proud of?

Dear Mom

What's your favourite homemade meal?

·Dear Daughter·

What's your favourite homemade meal?

Dear Mom

What makes you feel happy?

~ · Dear Daughter · ~

What makes you feel happy?

Dear Mom

Describe your perfect day.

Dear Daughter

Describe your perfect day.

Dear Mom

What's your favourite movie of all time? Why?

~ · Dear Daughter · ~

What's your favourite movie of all time? Why?

Dear Mom

What are the five things you wish I knew about you?

~ · Dear Daughter · ~

What are the five things you wish I knew about you?

Dear Mom

What superpower do you already have?

~·Dear Daughter·~

What superpower do you already have?

Dear Mom

What is the best gift you have ever gotten?

Dear Daughter

What is the best gift you have ever gotten?

Dear Mom

How do you feel about brothers and sisters?

·Dear Daughter·

How do you feel about brothers and sisters?

Dear Mom

Which famous person would you like to meet?

Dear Daughter

Which famous person would you like to meet?

Dear Mom

What is the one thing you couldn't live without?

~ · Dear Daughter · ~

What is the one thing you couldn't live without?

Dear Mom

What's your all time favourite song?

~ ·Dear Daughter· ~

What's your all time favourite song?

Dear Mom

Who do you admire and why?

·Dear Daughter·

Who do you admire and why?

Dear Mom

What's your dream birthday gift?

~•·Dear Daughter·•~

What's your dream birthday gift?

Dear Mom

When you are sad how do you make yourself feel better?

~ ·Dear Daughter· ~

When you are sad how do you make yourself feel better?

Dear Mom

What is your favourite thing about yourself?

·Dear Daughter·

What is your favourite thing about yourself?

Dear Mom

Do you prefer cake or ice cream?

Dear Daughter

Do you prefer cake or ice cream?

Dear Mom

What is the silliest thing you have ever done?

·Dear Daughter·

What is the silliest thing you have ever done?

Dear Mom

What is something that embarasses you alot?

- -

- -

- -

- -

- -

- -

- -

- -

Dear Daughter

What is something that embarasses you alot?

Dear Mom

What is something you look for in a friend?

Dear Daughter

What is something you look for in a friend?

Dear Mom

What is something that really confuses you?

- -

- -

- -

- -

- -

- -

- -

- -

·Dear Daughter·

What is something that really confuses you?

Dear Mom

What do you remember most about the past year?

~ ·Dear Daughter· ~

What do you remember most about the past year?

Dear Mom

What is it that you learned from me?

·Dear Daughter·

What is it that you learned from me?

Dear Mom

What is it that you dont want me to forget?

~ ·Dear Daughter· ~

What is it that you dont want me to forget?

Dear Mom

Thank you for.....

Dear Daughter

Thank you for.....

We have reached the end!

End Date:

__ / __ / ___

One word which describes my mom the best ....

One word which describes my daughter the best ....